KS2 SCIENCE

Ages 7-9

Peter Riley

Educational consultant: Ann Dicks

Illustrated by Rob Davis/www.the-art-agency.co.uk
and Tom Connell/www.the-art-agency.co.uk

First published by Parragon in 2009

Parragon
Queen Street House
4 Queen Street
Bath BA1 1HE, UK

ISBN 978-1-4075-3784-9

Printed in Malaysia

Notes to parents

The Gold Stars® Key Stage 2 series

The Gold Stars® Key Stage 2 series has been created to help your child revise and practise key skills and information learned in school. Each book is a complete companion to the Key Stage 2 curriculum and has been written by an expert team of teachers. The books will help to prepare your child for the SATS tests that they take in Year 6.

The books also support Scottish National Guidelines 5-14.

How to use this book

- Do talk about what's on the page. Let your child know that you are sharing the activities. Talking about the sections that introduce and revise essential information is particularly important. Usually children will be able to do the fill-in activities fairly independently.

- Keep work times short. Do leave a page that seems too difficult and return to it later.

- It does not matter if your child does some of the pages out of turn.

- Your child does not need to answer the questions in complete sentences.

- Check your child's answers using the answer section on pages 60-63. Give lots of praise and encouragement and remember to reward effort as well as achievement.

- Do not become anxious if your child finds any of the pages too difficult. Children learn at different rates.

Contents

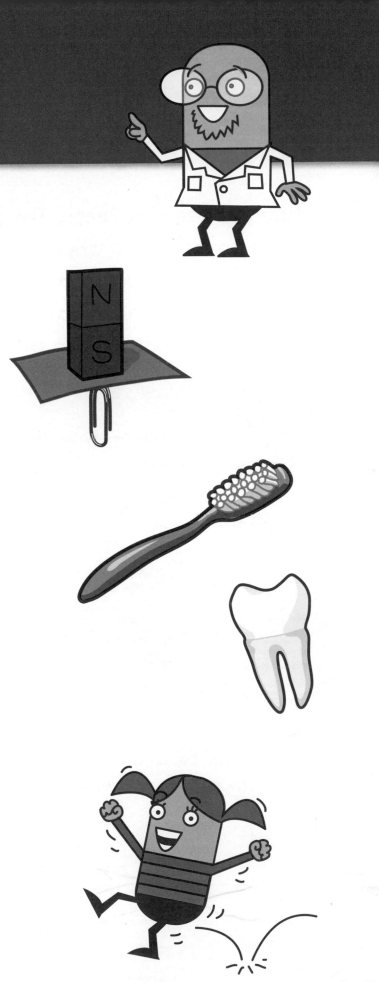

Solids and liquids

Friction

Electricity

Teeth

Learning objective: To recognize different types of teeth and know what they do.

We have two sets of teeth. The first ones are called milk teeth and we begin to lose them when we are about seven. The second set are called permanent teeth and you can keep them all your life if you look after them. The purpose of the teeth is to break up food into small pieces so that we can swallow it.

Types of teeth

There are three types of teeth. They are incisors, canines and molars.

An incisor tooth is chisel shaped for cutting up soft foods such as fruit.

A canine tooth is pointed for tearing tougher food such as meat.

Molar teeth have lumpy tops, which grind together when you chew and mash up the food into tiny pieces.

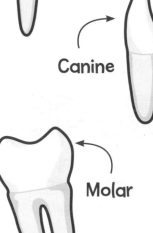

Incisor

Canine

Molar

A

Match the tooth with its purpose by drawing a line between them.

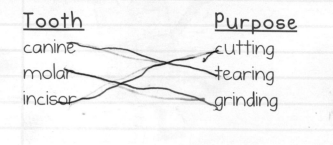

Tooth	Purpose
canine	cutting
molar	tearing
incisor	grinding

Look in a mirror and identify the three different types of teeth in your mouth.

The care of teeth

Learning objective: To know how to keep teeth healthy.

If you do not clean your teeth a sticky coating covers them. It is called plaque. Microbes settle in the plaque and feed on sugar in your food. They make acid. This rots the teeth. When you clean your teeth, the brush scrapes off the plaque so the microbes have nowhere to live and the toothpaste stops the work of the acid.

Remember to clean the back of your teeth as well as the front. You should not eat or drink anything after you have cleaned your teeth at night because the microbes will start feeding again.

During the day eat hard foods such as celery, raw carrots or crunchy apples as snacks, to help keep your teeth clean.

DEFINITION

microbes Tiny forms of life that can only be seen with a microscope. We call harmful microbes germs.

acid A substance that can break up other substances.

B

Choose the correct words to fill in the spaces in the sentences below.

microbes   healthy   clean   coating   teeth   acid   plaque

Plaque is a sticky _microbes_ that covers the teeth. _plaque acid_ live in it and make _coating_ that rots your _teeth_ . When you _clean_ your teeth you remove the acid and _plaque_ and keep your teeth _healthy_

Food groups

There are hundreds of different foods but they can be sorted into four food groups.

Meat and fish
Lamb, beef, chicken, salmon, tuna

Fruit and vegetables
Apple, orange, pear, mango, potatoes, carrots, cabbage, onions, peas, carrots

Carbohydrates
Rice, pasta, bread

Fats and sugars
Butter, cheese, sweets, biscuits

DEFINITION

carbohydrate A substance made by plants that gives you energy. It is sometimes called starch. Rice and pasta are carbohydrates.

Which group is your favourite food in?

A

To which food group does each of the foods in this meal belong? Write the name of each item and the group.

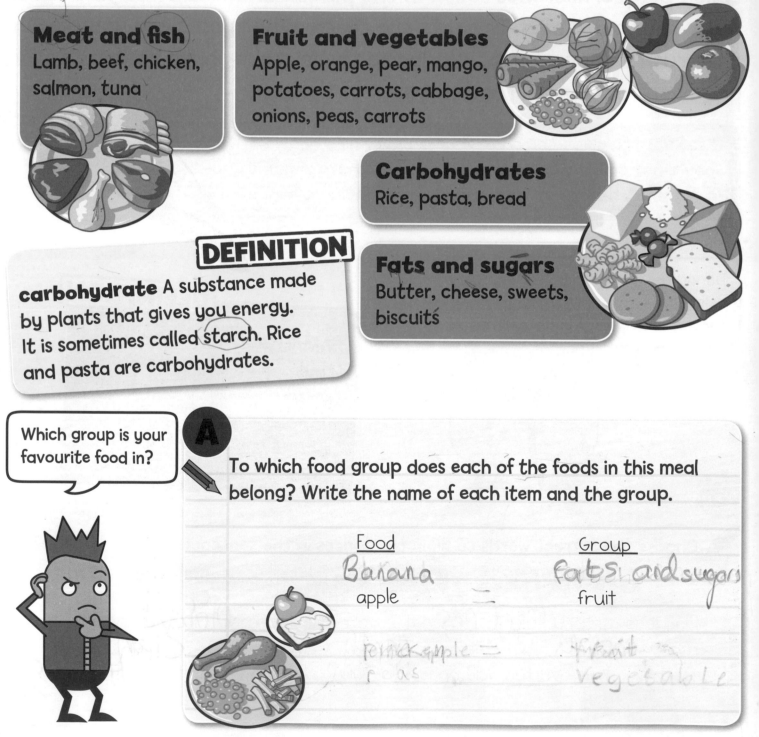

Food	Group
Banana	Fats and sugars
apple	fruit
pineapple	fruit
peas	vegetable

How the body uses food

The foods in each group help the body in a special way.

Healthy eating

To keep really healthy you need to eat different amounts of the foods in the different groups. This pyramid of food can help you remember to eat the correct amounts of food. Eat only small amounts of food at the top of the pyramid and larger amounts of the food lower down.

Fats and sugars give the body energy for action but are not good for you in large quantities.

Meat and fish help the body to grow and to repair its injuries.

Carbohydrates give the body energy for action.

Fruit and vegetables are maintenance foods. They help keep all parts of the body healthy and working well.

B

Draw a line between each food and the way it helps the body.

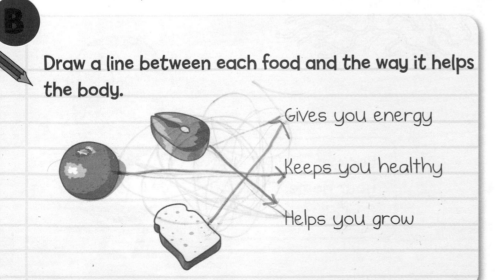

Gives you energy

Keeps you healthy

Helps you grow

Do you eat healthily like the pyramid suggests?

9

The parts of a plant

Learning objective: To know and recognize the parts of a plant.

There are four main parts to a plant. They are the root, stem, leaf and flower.

The flower
A plant may have one or more flowers. The large brightly coloured parts of a flower are called the petals.

The leaf
A plant has many leaves. Most are green but some may have white or coloured parts.

The stem
The stems of many plants are green and bendy. The stem of a tree is made of wood and covered in bark. It is called the trunk.

The root
Roots are white and spread out through the soil.

Look at a plant in your home. Can you find all its parts?

What the plant parts do

Learning objective: To learn the purpose of each part of the plant.

Each plant part has an important task to do in the life of the plant.

The flower
The flower makes pollen which is carried away by insects or the wind. The flower also receives pollen from other flowers of the same kind and uses it to make seeds.

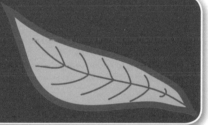

The leaf
The leaf makes food from the water it receives from the stem, from the air around it and from the sunlight shining on it. The food is used to make all parts of the plant grow.

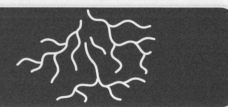

The stem
The stem holds up the leaves and flowers and carries water and food to all parts of the plant.

The roots
The roots hold the plant in the ground and take up water and minerals that the plant needs to make food.

A

1. Move your finger over the picture of the plant opposite to show the way water moves through the plant.

2. Move your finger again to show how food moves.

DEFINITION

minerals Substances in the soil that the plant takes in to stay healthy.

Plant growth

Learning objective: To know experiments can be made to investigate plant growth.

Plant growth can be investigated by making fair tests on the effects of leaves, light, water and warmth.

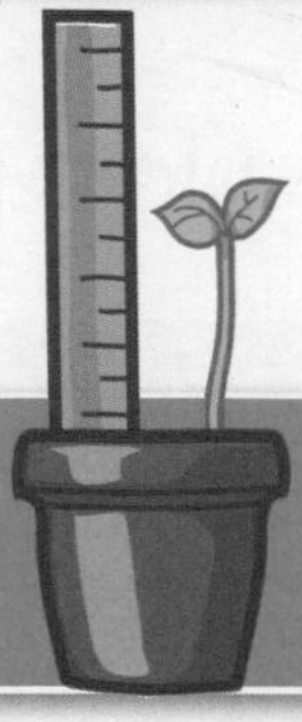

How to measure growth

The length of the stem can be measured to show how a plant grows.

Experiment 1: Investigating leaves and plant growth

Two plants were given the same amount of water, light and warmth but every time one plant sprouted leaves they were carefully cut off.

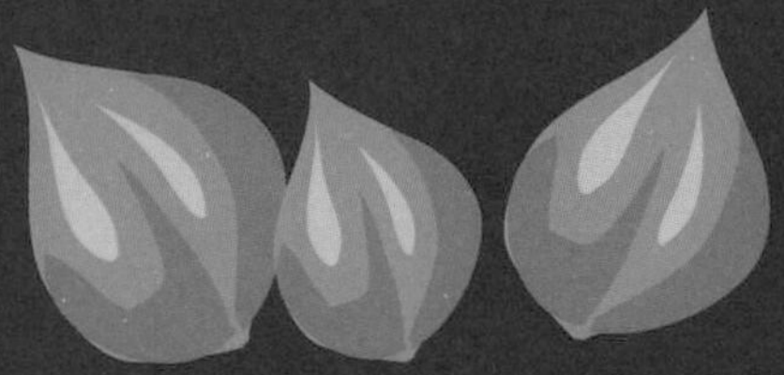

Experiment 2: Investigating light and plant growth

One plant was put in a cupboard and one plant was kept on a table near a sunny window. The picture shows how the plants looked after two weeks.

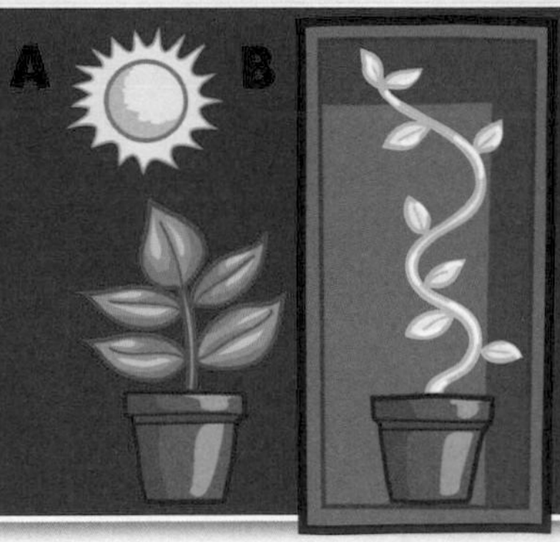

A

1. How do you think the two plants in experiment 1 compared after the experiment had run for two weeks?

2. In experiment 2, why do you think the leaves on plant B are yellow?

   I think its yellow because a plant needs its sun

3. In experiment 2, why do you think plant B has grown so tall?

Have a go at the experiments on this page yourself.

Experiment 3: Investigating water and plant growth

Five pots of cress seedlings were set up and watered each day. Different volumes of water were given to each pot as the table shows. After two weeks the plants were examined and their stems were measured.

Amount of water per day (cm³)	Stem length (cm)
5	O (dead)
10	3.5
15	7
20	3
25	O (dead)

Experiment 4: Investigating warmth and plant growth

A greenhouse traps the Sun's heat and makes a warm surrounding for plants. Two pots of cress seedlings were set up and the seedlings in one pot were covered with a transparent plastic cup to make a mini greenhouse. The picture shows how the pots looked after a week.

B

1. What do the results of experiment 3 show? Experiment 3 shows that plants need a bit of water and sun.

2. What is the effect of warmth on plant growth? the effect is to see that warmth makes plant g focothe cycle better

Introducing materials

Learning objective: To know that objects are made from 'different' materials.

We use many different materials to make the things we need.

Material	Use
wood	doors, furniture, bowls, spoons
brick	walls, fireplaces
stone	walls, stones
metal	pans, cutlery, cars, cans
plastic	bowls, toys, bottles, cases for computers
pottery	bowls, plant pots, ornaments
glass	windows, bottles, spectacles
cloth	clothes, blankets, towels
rubber	wellington boots, balls, tyres
paper	newspapers, books, envelopes

DEFINITION

material
A substance that can be used to make something.

A Use the table to answer the questions.

1. Name two materials used to make walls.

   brick and stone

2. Name three materials used to make bowls.

   plastic pottery and glass

3. Name three materials used to make a car.

   metal rubber and glass

4. Which materials can you see in the picture on the right? metal, cloth, wood, and pottery.

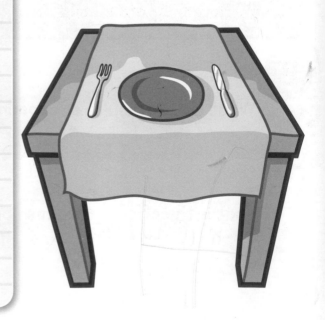

The properties of materials

Learning objective: To know that each material has properties.

Every material has some features called properties. It is the properties of a material that can make it useful to us.

Property	Examples of material with the property
hard	brick, stone, pottery
soft	cloth, plastic, foam
rough	stone, sandpaper
smooth	pottery, glass
shiny	metal, glass
dull	brick, stone
bendy	wood, rope
rigid	glass, brick

Look around you. How many of the materials in this table can you spot?

B

1. What are the properties of stone?

    rough

2. Which material is rigid, smooth and shiny?

    glass, brick, pottery, metal

3. Some materials do not let water pass through them. They are called waterproof materials. Other materials are not waterproof: they let water pass through them. Circle the items that are made from waterproof materials.

    A   B   C   D   E   F   G

Testing wear and hardness

Learning objective: To learn how fair tests are performed on materials.

Materials can be tested for wear and hardness by performing fair tests.

Experiment 1: Test for wear

Materials can be tested for wear with a small sheet of sandpaper stuck to a piece of wood. (The wood makes the sandpaper easier to hold as it is rubbed on the materials.) The test is made fair by rubbing the sandpaper the same number of times on each material. The material is examined with a magnifying glass to observe the amount of wear.

A   B   C

Experiment 2: Test for hardness

The hardness of a material can be tested by dropping a piece of soft modelling clay onto it. To make the test fair the ball should be dropped from the same height each time. The material which flattens a side of the ball the most is the hardest.

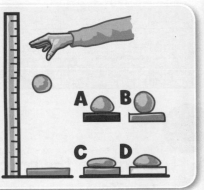

A   B
C   D

A

1. Which material in experiment 1 shows the most wear and which shows the least? the material B is the most wear and A is the least wear

2. Write the materials A to D in experiment 2 in order of hardness, starting with the hardest.
   1. C is hardest (hardest)
   2. D is second hardest
   3. A is third hardest
   4. the softest is B (softest)

The waterproof test

Learning objective: To learn how fair tests are performed on materials.

Materials can be tested to see if they are waterproof by pouring water on them and seeing if any water passes through.

Waterproof test

Materials can be tested to see if they are waterproof by laying them on paper towels then adding the same amount of water to each one. They should all be left for the same amount of time before they are lifted off the towel. If a material is waterproof there will not be a wet mark on the towel.

A
B
C
D
E

B

The paper towels A–E show the wet marks left after the waterproof test was applied to five different materials.

You can try all these tests yourself!

1. Which materials are waterproof?

   A and C

2. Which materials are not waterproof?

   D, B and E

3. Do all the materials which are not waterproof let through the same amount of water?

4. Explain your answer to question 3.

Types of rock

Learning objective: To learn about the three types of rock.

There are three types of rock. They form in different ways.

Igneous rocks

Igneous rocks form deep in the Earth where it is very hot. Basalt is black. Granite is white speckled with black and pink spots.

Metamorphic rocks

These form from other rocks that have slipped deep into the Earth and been heated up. Slate is made from grey mud and breaks up into thin sheets. Some marble is made from crystals that shine like sugar.

Sedimentary rocks

These are formed from small particles that have stuck together. Sandstone is yellow and forms from grains of sand. Limestone is grey and forms from the shells of sea creatures. Chalk is white and made from the shells of very tiny sea creatures.

D   E

A   B   C   F   G

A

Read the descriptions of each type of rock and look at the pictures. Write down the letter of each rock next to its name.

Basalt	F	Limestone	b	Marble	C
Granite	g	Chalk	E		
Sandstone	A	Slate	d		

Can you find any of these rocks around your home?

The properties of rocks

Learning objective: To learn how the properties of rocks can be tested.

Rocks can be tested for hardness and the way they react with water.

Hardness test

The hardness of two rocks can be compared by rubbing them together over white card. The rock that crumbles less is the harder.

Water test

Some rocks have tiny spaces called pores inside them and let water move through them. Other rocks do not have any pores and water cannot move through them. Dry rocks can be tested by pouring a spoonful of water onto the top of them. If the rock is **porous** the water disappears into it but if the rock is **non-porous** the water remains on the top.

B

1. Look at the table and fill in the last column.

Rock	Water on rock	Porous/non-porous
Granite	Stays on top	non porous
Limestone	Sinks into rock	porous
Sandstone	Sinks into rock	porous
Basalt	Stays on top	non porous

DEFINITION

porous Having tiny spaces in it called pores.

2. Slate has been used to make the roof of houses. Do you think it is porous or non-porous? Why?

Soil

Soil is made from a mixture of particles of rock and humus. Soils vary from place to place.

Comparing the parts of a soil

The parts of a soil can be compared by filling a fifth of a jar with soil, nearly filling the jar with water then stirring it up for about a minute. When the water stops moving the humus floats and the rocky particles sink to the bottom. The particles at the bottom separate into layers.

humus

clay

silt

sand

Sieving soil

A sieve can then be used to separate soil particles of different sizes. The larger particles stay in the sieve and the smaller particles pass through the holes.

sand

For example, the sieve on the right has holes that are large enough for clay and silt to pass through but not large enough for the sand particles to pass through.

clay and silt

DEFINITION

humus The rotted remains of dead plants.

You could stir up potting compost and water then let it settle to compare its parts.

A

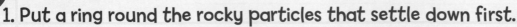

1. Put a ring round the rocky particles that settle down first.

    clay   sand   silt

2. Put a ring round the rocky particles that settle down last.

    clay   sand   silt

3. How do you think clay and silt could be separated?

The drainage of soil

Learning objective: To learn how drainage is compared in a fair test.

When water falls on the soil it goes down into spaces between the particles. If the spaces are large the water passes through the soil quickly and we say the soil drains well. If the spaces are small the water passes less quickly and we say the soil drains poorly.

Comparing the drainage of soils.

The drainage of different soils can be compared in the following way:

A Put the same amount of each soil in a filter funnel lined with filter paper.

B Pour the same amount of water on each soil sample.

C After five minutes measure how much water has passed through.

$100cm^3$ of water was added to four soil samples and the water was collected and measured after five minutes. This table shows the results.

Soil sample	Water added (cm^3)	Water drained (cm^3)	Water still in the soil (cm^3)
A	100	60	
B	100	43	
C	100	71	

1. How much soil was left in each soil after five minutes? Fill in the table above.

2. Which soil has the best drainage: A, B or C?

3. Which soil has the worst drainage: A, B or C?

Magnets and materials

Learning objective: To learn about magnets and magnetic / non-magnetic materials

Near each end of a magnet is a place where the magnetic force is stronger. These places are called the poles of a magnet. If a magnet is placed on cork and allowed to float on water it lines up with one pole pointing to the North Pole of the Earth. This is called the magnet's north pole. The other pole of the magnet is called the south pole.

When two magnets meet.

When the poles of two magnets are brought together they may join together because they **attract** each other or they may spring apart because they **repel** each other.

Here is what happens when two magnets are brought together in three different ways:

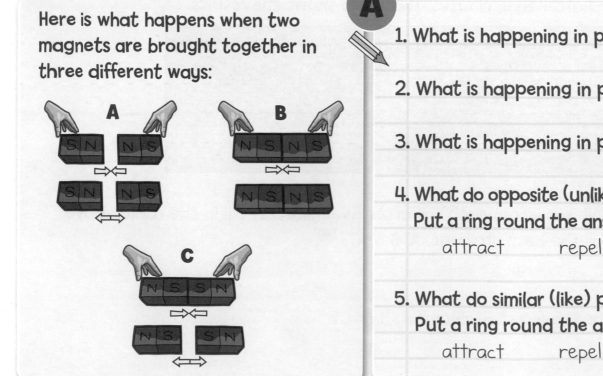

A

1. What is happening in picture A?

2. What is happening in picture B?

3. What is happening in picture C?

4. What do opposite (unlike) poles do? Put a ring round the answer.
   attract   repel

5. What do similar (like) poles do? Put a ring round the answer.
   attract   repel

Can you make fridge magnets attract and repel each other?

Testing materials

The materials in an object can be tested by bringing a magnet close to them. Only objects made of iron and steel will stick to a magnet. Iron and steel are magnetic materials. Other materials such as pottery, wood, cloth and plastic are not.

A magnet and cardboard

If a paperclip is put on one side of a piece of cardboard and a magnet on the other, the paperclip will stick to the cardboard. This happens because the force of the magnet acts through the cardboard. If the magnet is moved the paperclip on the other side moves too.

Testing the strength of magnets

The strength of a magnetic pole can be tested by attaching one paperclip after another to make a chain. The strength can also be found by placing more and more sheets of cardboard between a magnetic pole and a paperclip until the paperclip falls away.

B

1. In the paperclip test above which magnet was the strongest?

2. Which was the weakest?

3. When the three magnets were tested with sheets of cardboard, which magnet do you think needed the most sheets of cardboard to make the paperclip fall away?

Springs

There are two types of common springs: a close-coiled spring where the coils touch each other and an open-coiled spring where the coils do not touch.

Close-coiled springs and forces

If you stretch a close-coiled spring, a tension force forms in the spring. You can feel it pulling on your fingers. This force pulls the spring back to its original length when you let go of one end. You cannot squash a close-coiled spring because the coils are already touching.

Pull

1   2   3

Tension force

Open-coiled springs and forces

When you squash an open-coiled spring a compression force forms in the spring. You can feel it pushing on your fingers. This force pushes the spring back to its original length when you let go of one end. You can also stretch an open-coiled spring just like you can a close-coiled spring.

Push

1   2   3

Compression force

A

1. What will happen if a weight is put on top of spring A and then spring B?

2. What will happen if a weight is hung from spring A and then spring B?

A   B

Elastic bands

Learning objective: To learn that elastic bands generate forces when stretched.

When an elastic band is stretched by a pulling force in one direction a tension force develops in the elastic band to match it. The tension force pulls in the opposite direction. If the pulling force is removed the tension force pulls the elastic band back to its original shape.

A push meter
An elastic band can be used to make a push meter.

1. The elastic band is stretched between two nails and a scale is drawn on one side to measure the pushing force.
2. A toy car is pushed into the elastic band and its position is measured on the scale.
3. The car is then let go and it shoots away.
4. The distance it travels is measured.

Ask an adult to help you make your own push meter!

B

When a toy car is pushed back along the scale to 4 it shoots away 20 centimetres. How far do you think it would go if:

1. It was pushed along the scale to 1? Circle the correct answer.
    about 1cm   about 5cm   about 30cm
2. It was pushed along the scale to 6? Circle the correct answer.
    about 1cm   about 5cm   about 30cm

Light and shadows

Light is given out by a light source. It travels in straight lines. When light reaches most objects it is stopped from travelling and a shadow forms behind the object.

How light travels

You can see that light travels in straight lines by putting a comb across a torch and shining the torch across a sheet of paper.

Why shadows form

When light strikes an object and cannot pass through it, a shadow forms on the opposite side. It is black because the light is blocked and it has a similar shape to the object.

A

Look at this picture. From which torch is the light coming to make the shadow?

A   B   C

DEFINITION

light source Something that gives out light, such as the Sun, an electric lamp or a candle flame.

Materials and light

Light does not pass through most materials. However it does pass through a few.

Opaque materials stop light rays passing through them and cast dark shadows. You cannot see through them. Most materials are opaque.

Transparent materials let most of the light rays pass straight through them. You can see clearly through them and they cast pale shadows.

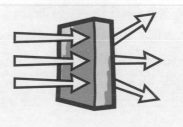

Translucent materials let some of the light rays through them but scatter them in all directions. You cannot see clearly through them and they make quite dark shadows.

B

Put an O in the boxes of materials that are opaque, a T in materials that are transparent and a TR in materials that are translucent.

clear plastic ☐   frosted glass ☐   greaseproof paper ☐

window glass ☐   brick ☐   orange juice ☐

wood ☐   cardboard ☐

water ☐   metal ☐

DEFINITION

light ray A very thin, straight beam of light.

The Sun and shadows

Learning objective: To know that as the Sun moves shadows change.

The Sun rises in the east, climbs in the sky until midday then slowly sinks in the west each day. As the Sun moves in the sky the shadows cast by objects change.

When the Sun is rising in the east long shadows are made which point towards the west.

When the Sun is at its highest at midday short shadows are made which point north.

When the Sun is sinking in the west, long shadows are made which point towards the east.

Remember never to look directly at the Sun. It can damage your eyes.

A

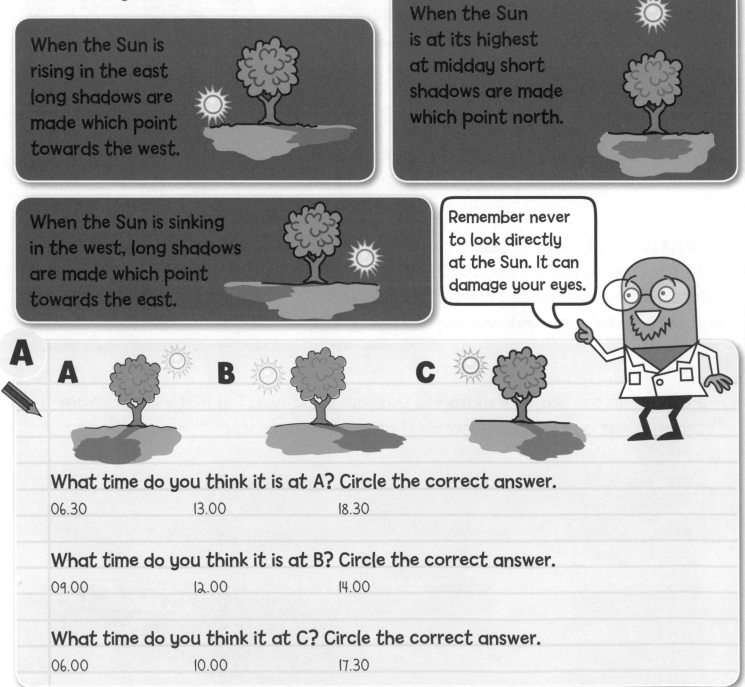

A   B   C

What time do you think it is at A? Circle the correct answer.
06.30   13.00   18.30

What time do you think it is at B? Circle the correct answer.
09.00   12.00   14.00

What time do you think it at C? Circle the correct answer.
06.00   10.00   17.30

How shadows change

Learning objective: To link the height of a light source with shadow length.

Scientists sometimes make models in order to experiment. In this experiment the torch is a model Sun and the block is a model of a tree.

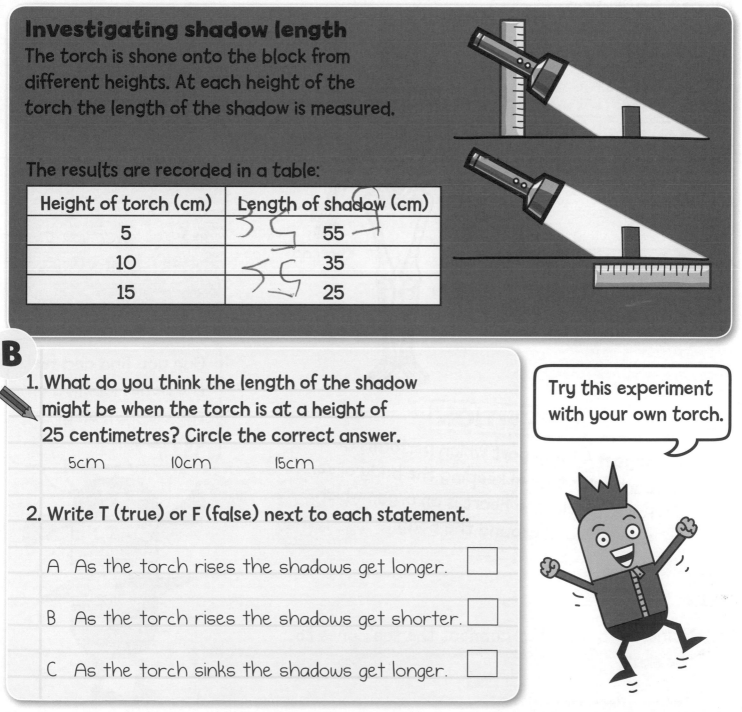

Investigating shadow length

The torch is shone onto the block from different heights. At each height of the torch the length of the shadow is measured.

The results are recorded in a table:

Height of torch (cm)	Length of shadow (cm)
5	55
10	35
15	25

B

1. What do you think the length of the shadow might be when the torch is at a height of 25 centimetres? Circle the correct answer.

   5cm   10cm   15cm

2. Write T (true) or F (false) next to each statement.

   A   As the torch rises the shadows get longer. ☐

   B   As the torch rises the shadows get shorter. ☐

   C   As the torch sinks the shadows get longer. ☐

Try this experiment with your own torch.

The human skeleton

Learning objective: To learn about the parts of the human skeleton.

The human skeleton has 206 bones. They work together to support the body and help it move. Some bones protect some of the organs of the body too.

The skull is made from a group of bones that protect the brain.

The shoulder blade and collar bone attach the arm bones to the spine.

The ribs form a cage which protects the heart and lungs and moves to help us breathe.

The pelvis attaches the leg bones to the spine.

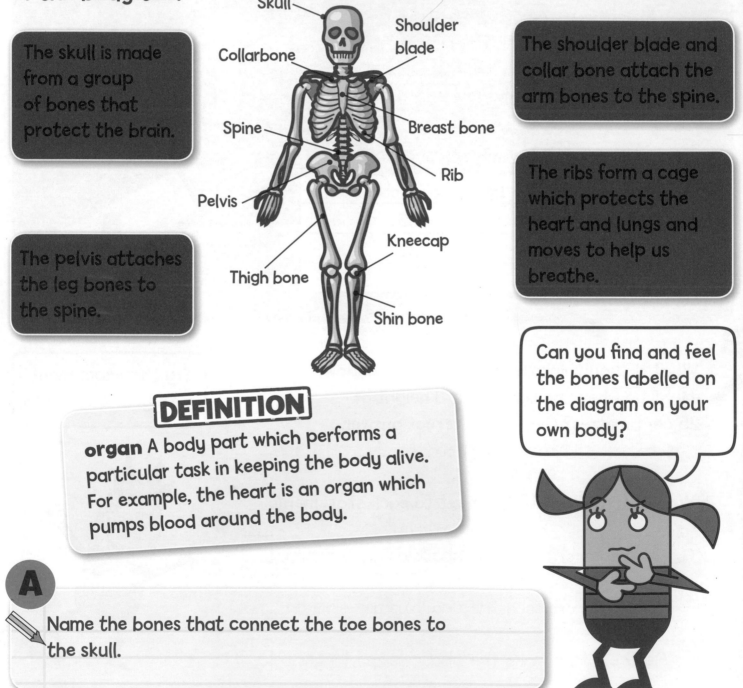

Skull
Shoulder blade
Collarbone
Spine
Breast bone
Rib
Pelvis
Kneecap
Thigh bone
Shin bone

Can you find and feel the bones labelled on the diagram on your own body?

DEFINITION

organ A body part which performs a particular task in keeping the body alive. For example, the heart is an organ which pumps blood around the body.

A

Name the bones that connect the toe bones to the skull.

Animal skeletons

Many animals have bony skeletons but some have skeletons made of shell, a horn-like material or even water.

Bony skeletons

Fish, amphibians, reptiles (scaly-skinned animals), birds and mammals (animals with hair) have bony skeletons with a skull and a spine. Fish have bones that support their fins, and reptiles such as snakes do not have arm or leg bones.

Animals with a skeleton of armour

Some animals have a skeleton made from hard material on the outside of their bodies. Crabs and shrimps have a skeleton made of shell. Insects and spiders have a skeleton made from a substance with properties similar to horn and finger nails.

Animals with a water skeleton

Earthworms and slugs have spaces in their bodies that are full of water. These spaces act like a water skeleton and support the body.

B

Match the animal to its skeleton by drawing lines between them.

slug

frog   skeleton of bone

shrimp   skeleton of armour

spider   water skeleton

snake

DEFINITION

amphibian An animal with a smooth skin, which has a tadpole stage in its life e.g. a frog.

Movement

Muscles can contract themselves, but they cannot stretch themselves. A contracting muscle can give a bone a pull and this can make part of the body move. To make the body part move back to its original position you need a second muscle.

Pairs of muscles

There are pairs of muscles all over the body that contract, move body parts and help each other stretch. One example of a pair of muscles are those in the upper arm. They are called the biceps and the triceps.

1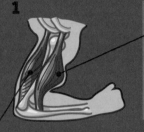

The biceps contracts and pulls on the bones of the lower arm to raise them.

The triceps is stretched by the contracting biceps.

2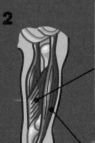

The triceps contracts and pulls on the bones of the lower arm to lower them.

The biceps is stretched by the contracting triceps.

Stretch out your right arm. Spread out the fingers of your left hand and press them into your biceps. Bend your right arm. What do you feel with your fingers?

DEFINITION

contract To make shorter.

Exercise

Exercise is any activity that makes the body move about. Exercise helps the body stay healthy.

Keep an exercise diary for a week. Write down what you did and how long you did it.

Exercise keeps bones and joints strong. It makes the muscles strong, too.

The heart

The heart is a bag of muscle that pumps the blood round the body. The blood takes food and oxygen to all parts of the body. When the muscles exercise they need more food and oxygen and the heart pumps faster to provide them. This makes the heart muscles stronger, too.

Exercise and fat

The body stores energy from food as fat. Too much fat makes the body so heavy that it strains the muscles and heart to move. Exercise uses up energy and stops the body getting overweight.

DEFINITION

joints The places where bones are joined together such as at the elbow or the knee.

A

Name five ways in which exercise makes the body healthy.

Did you do more exercise or less exercise than you thought? Do you need to do more?

The size of habitats

Learning objective: To know that organisms live in habitats.

The place where an organism lives is called its habitat. There are different sizes of habitat.

Micro habitat

This is the smallest type of habitat. It could be the place under a stone where a centipede lives or the underside of a leaf, which is home to greenfly.

Mini habitat

This is made up from many micro habitats. A bush is a mini habitat. It has micro habitats, which include the bark where beetles live, leaves where caterpillars feed, flowers where spiders may hide to catch insects and roots where eelworms gather to feed.

Habitat

This is the largest habitat and is made up from micro and mini habitats. A forest is a habitat that is made up from trees, bushes, grassy areas and bare ground covered with dead leaves.

A

A   B   C   D

(the space under the rock)

Identify A–D by putting a ring around your answer.

What is A?	habitat	mini habitat	micro habitat
What is B?	habitat	mini habitat	micro habitat
What is C?	habitat	mini habitat	micro habitat
What is D?	habitat	mini habitat	micro habitat

DEFINITION

organism A living thing such as a plant or an animal.

The conditions in a habitat

Learning objective: To know that organisms in a habitat are adapted to its conditions.

There are many different kinds of habitat. Each one has a set of conditions, which organisms must be adapted to if they are to survive there.

The forest habitat

The trees make the forest shady, so only plants that are adapted to growing in dim light such as ferns and mosses can grow on the ground there.

The pond habitat

The poorly draining soil causes a deep pool to form. Only organisms adapted to living in water can survive there.

The rocky shore habitat

Only organisms which are adapted to the beating of the waves and living in pools of salty water can survive in this habitat.

The limpet has a sucker to grip the rock and its shell stops it losing water when the tide is out.

The crab breathes in salty water and can hide away when the tide comes in.

The swellings called bladders on the seaweed make most of the plant float and stay in the light to make food. The seaweed has a holdfast, which looks like a root, to grip the rock.

B

1. Meadow grass is adapted to growing in bright light. Explain what would happen to it if it was planted in a wood and why.

2. Describe what would happen to a limpet if it could not grip onto the rocks.

Grouping living things

Learning objective: To use the features of organisms to put them into groups.

Every organism has features, which can be used to put it into a group with other organisms. Organisms are placed in groups because it makes them easier for scientists to study.

Here are some major groups of animals and their features:

Animal group	Features
Insects	Six legs
Spiders	Eight legs
Fish	Scales and fins
Amphibians	Smooth slimy skin
Reptiles	Scaly skin
Birds	Feathers
Mammals	Hair or fur

You could also check out the definition of **amphibian** on page 31.

A

1. Write the letter of each animal next to the group it belongs to.

Animal group	Animal
Insects	
Spiders	
Fish	
Amphibians	
Reptiles	
Birds	
Mammals	

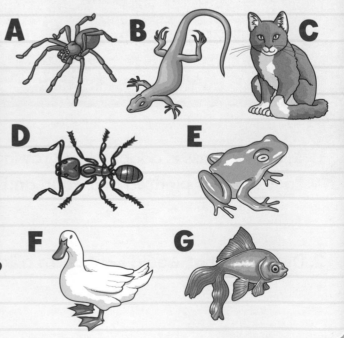

2. Which animal group do humans belong to?

Keys

Learning objective: To learn how to use a key to identify organisms.

A key is a number of features about organisms, which is set out in a series of questions. As each answer is made you move onto the next question until you find the identity of the organism.

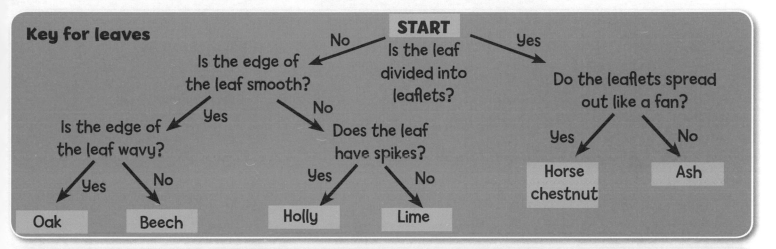

For example, in this key if you look at leaf **F** below and begin to answer questions about it you will see that it is not divided into leaflets, that its edge is not smooth and it does not have spikes. This means that the leaf belongs to a lime tree.

B

Use the key to identify the leaves.

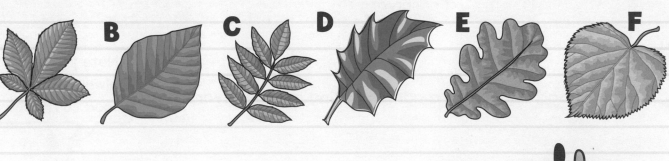

A

B

C

D

E

F

37

Food chains

Learning objective: To understand food chains.

Some organisms in a habitat make food and others eat it. Scientists use special words for organisms that make and eat food.

DEFINITION

producers Organisms that make food are called producers. Plants are producers.

consumers Organisms that eat food are called consumers. All animals are consumers. There are two kinds of consumer. A prey animal is one that is consumed by another animal. A predator is an animal that consumes another animal.

herbivores Herbivores eat plants and are prey animals.

carnivore Carnivores are meat-eaters and predators.

Organisms in a food chain

1. The first organism in a food chain is a plant. It makes food from air, sunlight and water.
2. The second organism is a herbivore. It is probably also a prey animal.
3. The third animal in a food chain is a predator.

Food chains can have more than three organisms in them. For example, if an eagle ate a fox it could be added to the food chain. This would mean that the fox is a prey animal as well as a predator, but it would still remain a carnivore.

A

1. Draw a food chain with a human acting as a herbivore.

2. Draw a food chain with a human acting as a carnivore.

Note that the arrow always goes from the food to the feeder.

Protecting habitats

Learning objective: To understand the significance of protecting habitats.

Plants and animals come to live together in a habitat because they are adapted to the conditions there. If these conditions change the organisms are less well adapted and may die or move away.

When a forest is cut down

The trees provide mini habitats for many organisms so when the trees are removed the organisms are removed too. Predators such as woodpeckers that feed on insects in the bark do not have anything to eat and move away. The trees also provide shade so when they are removed strong light can reach the ground. Plants such as ferns are less adapted to these conditions and may die.

When a pond is drained

Animals such as fish, which cannot move away when the pond is drained, die. Frogs may hop away to find a new pond. Birds such as herons, which feed on fish and frogs, move away too. Water plants cannot survive in dry soil and die. Birds, which nested among the water plants, move away.

Find out why the Earth's rainforests need protecting and make a poster about it.

DEFINITION

habitat The place where an animal or plant lives.

B Imagine that there are plans to drain a pond and clear forest near your home. Write a letter or design a poster that protests about the plan and encourages people to conserve the habitats.

Temperatures

Learning objective: To learn how to use a thermometer and record temperatures.

A thermometer is used to measure temperature. The temperature is measured in degrees Celsius. Scientists write this as °C.

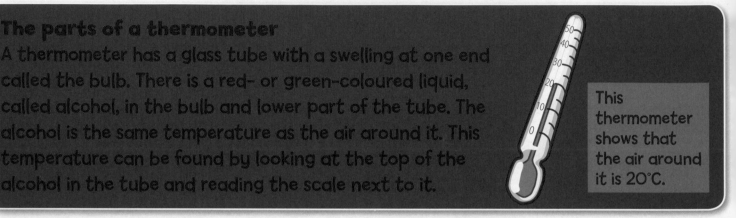

The parts of a thermometer

A thermometer has a glass tube with a swelling at one end called the bulb. There is a red- or green-coloured liquid, called alcohol, in the bulb and lower part of the tube. The alcohol is the same temperature as the air around it. This temperature can be found by looking at the top of the alcohol in the tube and reading the scale next to it.

This thermometer shows that the air around it is 20°C.

Taking the temperature

When taking the temperature of a liquid the thermometer bulb must be kept in it for a few moments before the reading is made. This gives the alcohol time to become as cold or as hot as the liquid. The thermometer bulb must be kept in the liquid while the scale is being read.

The thermometer shows the temperature of the water to be 25°C.

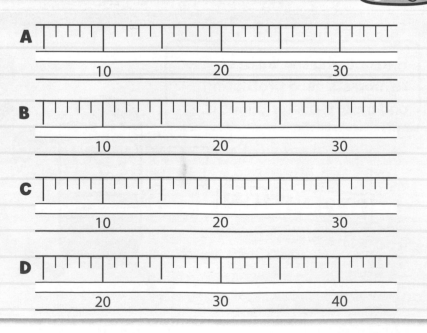

A

1. Shade in thermometer A to show a temperature of 30°C.

   A | 10 | 20 | 30

2. Shade in thermometer B to show a temperature of 25°C.

   B | 10 | 20 | 30

3. Shade in thermometer C to show a temperature of 33°C.

   C | 10 | 20 | 30

4. Shade in thermometer D to show a temperature of 39°C.

   D | 20 | 30 | 40

temperature
A measure of the coldness or hotness of something.

The temperatures of substances can change over a short period of time. These changes can be measured with a thermometer and a clock.

Recording temperature change
A cup of warm water was left to stand on a table for four minutes. The temperature of the water was taken five times to show how the temperature changed in this time.

B

1. Fill in this table from the data in the pictures.

Time from start (minutes)	Temperature (°C)

2. Why do you think the last two temperatures were the same?

3. Now make a line graph from the data in the table.

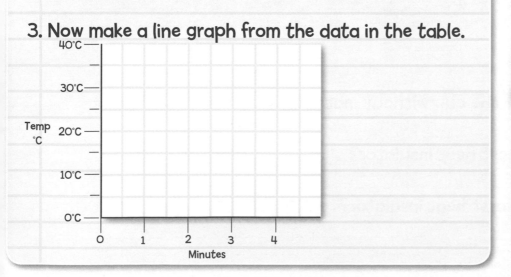

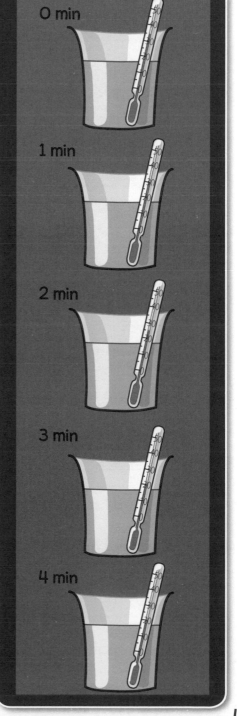

Heat insulators

Learning objective: To compare how materials prevent heat moving using a fair test.

Heat moves from a warmer place to a cooler place. A material which greatly slows down the movement of heat is called a heat insulator.

Testing for heat insulation

Materials are tested for their heat-insulating property in the following way. Plastic cups and their lids are covered with the materials but one cup and lid are left uncovered. The same amount of warm water is poured into each cup and the temperature is taken straight away and ten minutes later.

Wool   Aluminium foil   Cotton

  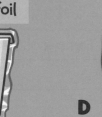 

A   B   C   D

The table shows how the temperature changed in each cup:

Time (Mins)	Cup A Temp (°C)	Cup B Temp (°C)	Cup C Temp (°C)	Cup D Temp (°C)
0	50	50	50	50
10	30	45	32	40

A

1. What is the purpose of the cup without material?

2. Which material is the best heat insulator?

3. Which material is the worst heat insulator?

Heat conductors

Learning objective: To compare how quickly materials move heat using a fair test.

A material which heat can move through quickly is called a heat conductor. When some materials, like butter, become hot they melt. This means that the melting of butter can be used as a rough measure for the movement of heat.

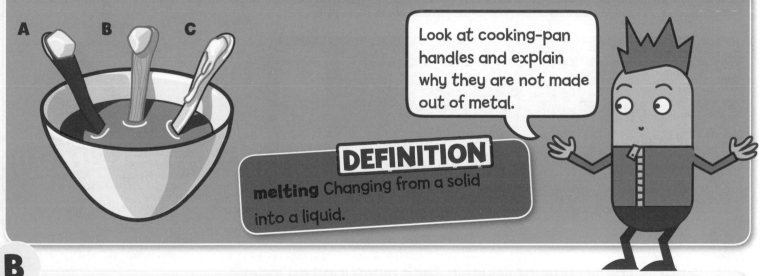

Testing for heat conduction
A test for heat conduction can be made by taking a plastic, wooden and steel spoon of the same size and placing them in a bowl of hot water. A small lump of butter is then added to the handle of each one and the lumps are watched for signs of melting. The lump of butter melts fastest on the spoon made out of the best heat conductor.

A   B   C

Look at cooking-pan handles and explain why they are not made out of metal.

DEFINITION

melting Changing from a solid into a liquid.

B

1. Which spoon is made from the best heat conductor, A, B or C?

2. If you made a spoon out of aluminium foil and used it in this in this experiment explain what would you think would happen.

3. How does the metal in cooking pans help food in the pans to cook?

Solids and liquids

Learning objective: To compare solids and liquids and measure their volumes.

The shape of solids and liquids

A solid has a fixed shape. This means its shape does not change if you leave it for a long time. It does not change its shape if you turn it over or put it on its side. Liquids do not have any shape. They take up the shape of any container they are poured into.

The volume of solids

If a solid is shaped like a block you can easily find its volume by measuring its height, width and length then multiplying them.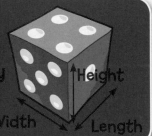

Take a block of wood and find its volume. Then look at another block of wood, estimate its volume then measure it. How good was your estimate?

Measuring the volume of a liquid

The volume of a liquid can be found by pouring it into a measuring cylinder, which is set on a flat horizontal surface. The eye should be brought level with the liquid surface for reading the volume on the scale of the cylinder.

DEFINITION

volume The amount of space taken up by a substance. Volume is measured in cubic centimetres (cm³).

A

1. What is the volume of liquid in each measuring cylinder?

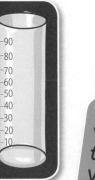

Volume in A:

Volume in B:

2. If the liquid from A is poured into B what will be the volume of liquid in B?

Flowing

Learning objective: To compare runniness in liquids and powdered solids.

Different liquids flow with different speeds. Their speeds can be compared in a runniness test. Tiny solid particles can also flow like liquids.

Comparing runniness
The runniness of liquids can be compared by letting them flow down a ramp and timing how long they take to reach the bottom.

Can you make salt or flour flow like a liquid?

Grains and powders
Some pieces of solid such as sand and salt are so small they form particles called grains. Some solid particles such as pepper and flour are even smaller and form powders. When grains or powder particles are put together into a group they slide over each other. This makes them flow and they can be poured like a liquid. They do not form a real liquid because they cannot form drops.

B

1. How is the runniness test made fair?

Pour water very slowly out of a jug and look for drops. What happens when you pour flour in the same way?

2. Here are the results when the runniness test was done on three liquids, A, B and C. Which one is water, which one is treacle and which one is vegetable oil? Fill in the table.

Liquid	Time to flow (seconds)	Identity of liquid
A	8	
B	20	
C	6	

Melting

If any solid is heated up enough it melts and becomes a liquid.

Melting

Solids keep their shapes at normal temperatures but if they are heated they may become soft and start to sag. If they are heated more strongly they flow and can form drops. When this happens they have turned into a liquid. The process in which a solid changes into a liquid is called melting. It is a reversible change.

For example, a candle is made from wax which melts when it gets hot and turns into a liquid.

A

Here are the melting points of four substances:

Substance	Melting point (°C)
A	200
B	750
C	430
D	850

DEFINITION

reversible change A change that can be reversed because it has an opposite. The opposite of melting is freezing.

melting point The temperature at which a solid melts is called its melting point.

1. The four substances are heated up in a furnace. What is the order in which they melt?

2. Which substances are still solid at 500°C?

3. When A melts, how much hotter must the furnace get before D melts?

Freezing

Learning objective: To know that when liquids are cooled down enough they freeze.

If any liquid is cooled down enough it freezes and becomes a solid.

Freezing

When a liquid freezes it cannot flow any more and takes on a fixed shape. It becomes a solid. Freezing is a reversible change.

For example, to make an ice lolly you put liquid water in a container in the freezer. As the water cools down it freezes. It becomes a solid and takes on the fixed shape of the container.

Freezing point

The temperature at which a liquid freezes is called its freezing point. This is the same as the melting point of the solid that it forms.

For example, the freezing point of the liquid called water is 0°C and is the same as the melting point of the solid, called ice, which it forms.

Different substances freeze at different temperatures. They do not all freeze at 0°C. The molten wax running down the side of a candle freezes when its temperature drops to 50°C.

What is the opposite of freezing?

B

Choose the correct words to fill in the spaces in the sentences below.

> hot   solid   side   liquid   600°C   flowing   freezing   away

The molten rock _____ down the _____ of a volcano is a _____ and may be as _____ as 1200°C. It cools as it moves _____ and when it reaches _____ it stops flowing and becomes _____ rock. The _____ point of the rock is 600°C.

Dissolving

Learning objective: To know that some solids dissolve in water and others do not.

When many solids are stirred up with water, they simply fall to the bottom of the liquid and form a layer. They do not dissolve. But some solids seem to disappear into the water when they are stirred up in it. These solids dissolve in the water.

Solids that do not dissolve
Sand, marbles, chalk and glass beads do not dissolve in water. They are said to be insoluble in water and form a layer at the bottom of the water container.

When a solid dissolves
When a solid such as sugar or salt dissolves in water it splits up into very tiny particles called atoms and molecules. They are so small that you would need a very powerful microscope to see them. The mixture of the water and the solid dissolved in it is called a solution.

Coloured solid, coloured solution
Some solids such as instant coffee granules are coloured. When they dissolve they colour the water, too.

DEFINITION

atoms The small particles from which everything is made. They can bunch together to form small groups called molecules.

A

1. Which of these substances dissolve in water? Tick the boxes.
   chalk ☐   sugar ☐   instant coffee granules ☐
   salt ☐   marble ☐   sand ☐

2. Loose tea leaves turn hot water brown but they also form a layer at the bottom of the cup or teapot. Explain what is happening.

Filtering

Learning objective: To understand how filtering can be used to separate materials.

A filter is a material with holes in it which can let a liquid pass through.

Filtering sand and water

When you pour water mixed with sand into a filter paper two things happen. The sand is held back in the paper because the grains are too big to go through the holes but the water passes through.

When salt water is filtered

When salt water is poured into a filter the salt does not settle in the paper. It is in such small pieces in the water that they pass through the holes with the water. A dissolved substance cannot be separated from water by filtering.

B

1. Some sand and sugar have been stirred into water. Explain what will happen to the sand, the sugar and the water when they are poured into a filter paper.

2. How could you tell that salt or sugar has been stirred into a cup of water if you cannot see it?

3. Is the paper in a tea bag a filter? Explain your answer.

49

The force meter

Learning objective: To learn how to use a force meter.

A force meter is made out of a close-coiled spring (see page 24). It is used to measure the strength of pulling forces. A force meter may also be called a spring balance or a newton meter.

The parts of a force meter

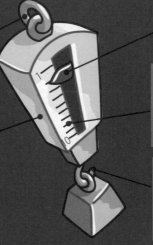

At the top of the force meter is a handle that can be attached to a hook or held in the hand.

Inside the force meter is the stretching part – a close-coiled spring.

Below the spring is a plastic rod with a pointer at its top.

Around the spring and rod is a plastic case with a scale on it. The units on the scale are newtons.

The plastic rod is attached to a hook. This can be attached to weights or items which are to be pulled.

How to measure a force

When the hook is pulled the spring stretches and the pointer moves down inside the case. When the pointer stops moving the size of the force can be measured by looking at the where the pointer has stopped on the scale.

DEFINITION

newton The unit in which forces are measured. One newton is about equal to the weight of an average sized apple.

A

What size of force does each of these force meters read?

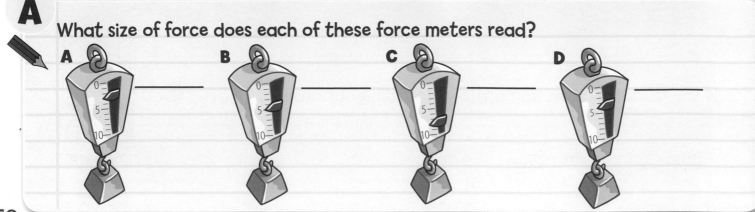

A _____   B _____   C _____   D _____

Friction

Learning objective: To learn about friction.

When you try and push your foot along a floor you can feel the force of friction.

Friction is a force generated when two surfaces touch and one is pushed or pulled over the other. Friction acts in the opposite direction to the pull or push. If the push or pull is weak the force of friction will match it in strength and the surfaces will not slide. When the push or pull reaches a certain strength it overcomes the force of friction and the surfaces move.

Push

Friction

A force meter and friction
A force meter can be used to find the force needed to overcome the force of friction.

A slope and friction
When a wood block is placed on a tray and one end raised slightly, gravity pulls on the block and friction holds the block in place. At some point, as the end is raised, gravity overcomes friction and the block slides. The height of the slope at which the block starts to slide is used to measure the force of friction.

Gravity

Friction

B

When the slope method was used to test the friction between an object and different materials on the slope the following readings were made:

Make a slope like the one on this page, put different shoes on it and tip it up. Which shoe has the best grip?

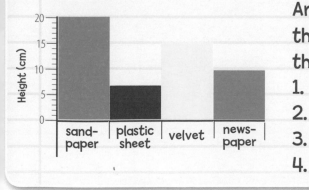

Arrange the materials in the order of the strength of friction between them and the block, strongest first.

1.

2.

3.

4.

Water resistance

Learning objective: To learn about water resistance and how to compare it.

When an object moves through water the water pushes back on it. This pushing force is called water resistance.

Streamlined shapes

A shape which allows water to flow over it easily is called a streamlined shape. Water resistance to this shape is low so the shape moves fast through the water. A spindle shape is a streamlined shape.

DEFINITION

spindle A rod which comes to a point at each end.

Comparing different shapes

The water resistance of different shapes of modelling clay can be compared using a tall cylinder of water and a stopclock.

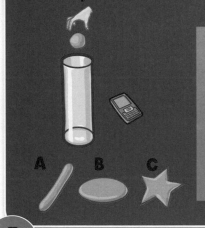

A   B   C

A piece of modelling clay is divided into three lumps of the same size then each lump is made into a different shape. Each shape is dropped down the cylinder and the time taken for it to fall to the bottom is recorded.

A

1. Which shape do you think went fastest and which went slowest?

2. How could the results be checked?

52

Air resistance

Air resistance is a pushing force which acts on an object as it moves through the air. The larger the surface moving through the air, the stronger the pushing force on the object.

> Running holding up a small piece of card is easy...

> ...but running holding up a big piece of card like this is hard! Try it and see!

Comparing air resistance

Model parachutes of different sizes can be used to investigate air resistance. They are all dropped from the same height of about 1.5 metres and the time for them to reach the ground is timed.

A   B   C

B

Three parachutes were made with square canopies and dropped from a height of 1.5 metres. Here are the results:

Parachute	Length of canopy side (cm)	Time of fall (seconds)
A	10	5
B	8	4
C	12	6

1. Which parachute took longest to fall?

2. Which parachute took the shortest time?

3. How long would you expect a parachute with 14-centimetre sides to fall? Circle the correct answer.   9 seconds   8 seconds   7 seconds

Electrical components

The items that make up an electrical circuit are called components. Here are the components that are used in simple circuits in science experiments. You must never use mains electricity for experiments.

Battery
This provides the electricity for use in circuits. It is sometimes called a cell. The button at one end is called the positive terminal and the base at the other end is called the negative terminal. The power of the battery is measured in volts (V). Batteries for science circuits should be 1.5 V.

+
1.5 V
−

Switch
This controls the flow of electricity in a circuit.

Switch open

Switch closed

Wires
These are made of metal and may be coated in plastic. They conduct electricity around the circuit. Some wires have crocodile clips on their ends.

Motor
When electricity flows through the motor it makes the motor shaft spin.

Buzzer
This makes a sound when electricity flows through it.

Lamp
This has a thin wire called a filament which lights up when electricity flows through it.

A

Match the component to its use by drawing lines between them:

motor   conducts electricity
wire   controls the flow of
                 electricity
buzzer   provides movement
switch   makes a sound

DEFINITION

circuit A loop made by joining electrical components together so that a current of electricity can flow through them.

Making a circuit

All electrical circuits need one or more batteries to provide the electric current. They need wires to connect the components together and a switch to control the flow. They also need either a lamp, buzzer or motor to tell you when the current is flowing.

Making connections
A circuit is made by connecting up the components. The connections need to be made carefully because if a gap is left between components or the components can easily separate a current will not flow. A gap between components can occur at any place in a circuit.

DEFINITION

electric current
The flow of electricity around a circuit.

Electricity will only flow in a circuit when all the connections are firmly made and the switch is switched on.

A

B

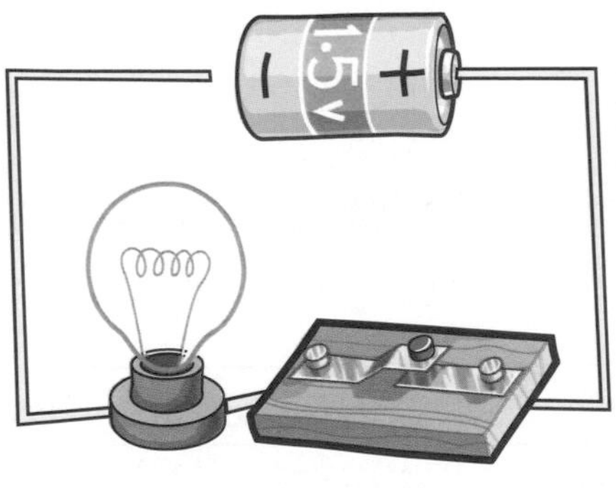

Electricity cannot flow through circuit B because the switch is open and because there is a gap in the wire.

B

Could electricity flow through this circuit? Explain your answer.

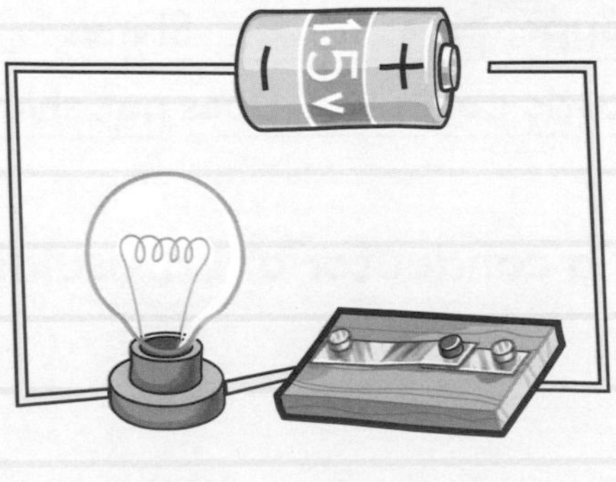

Testing for flow

Materials which let electricity flow through them are called electrical conductors. Materials which do not let electricity flow through them are called electrical insulators. A simple circuit can be used to test them.

Setting up the test circuit

Materials can be tested in this circuit. A material to be tested is placed across the gap and the switch is switched on. If the lamp lights, electricity is flowing around the circuit and through the material. This means that the material is a conductor. If the lamp does not light when the switch is switched on, the material is not allowing electricity to flow. This means the material is an insulator.

Place material to be tested here.

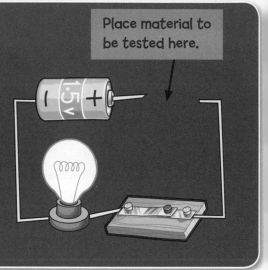

A

1. Which objects are made from materials that are conductors and which from materials that are insulators? Write your answers in the third column.

Object	Lamp	Conductor or insulator
Steel spoon	Shines	
Wooden spoon	Does not shine	
Copper pipe	Shines	
Plastic comb	Does not shine	

2. Is air a conductor or an insulator? Explain your answer.

Switches

A switch has two pieces of metal called contacts. When the switch is off, the metal contacts do not touch and the air between them acts as an insulator so a current of electricity does not flow. When the switch is on, the contacts touch and electricity flows round the circuit.

> If you have a torch, look and see if you have to press or slide the switch to complete the circuit and turn the torch on.

The importance of switches
You do not **have** to use a switch to make a circuit. It is possible just to wrap the ends of the wires together to complete a circuit. However it is better to use a switch because it does not wear out the ends of the wires and is quicker to use.

Paperclip switch
This type of switch is turned on when the paperclip is moved so it can touch both drawing pins.

Pressure switch
This type of switch is turned on when the two inside surfaces are pressed together. The two pieces of foil touch and let electricity flow. It can be used in a burglar alarm circuit. The switch could be under a mat so that it turns on if it is stepped on.

B

Explain how the switch on the right works.

Metal ball

Plastic casing

Wires

Using more batteries

A battery pushes a current of electricity around a circuit. Its pushing power is measured in volts (see page 54). A bulb is made to take a certain voltage of electricity. If it is too high the lamp will burn out.

Lining up batteries

A battery pushes electricity around a circuit from its negative terminal to its positive terminal. If another battery is added it must be placed with its positive terminal next to the negative terminal of the first battery. If batteries are lined up with both their positive or negative terminals together no current will flow.

Batteries and lamps

1. When two 1.5V batteries are correctly placed in a circuit their pushing power on the electricity rises to 1.5V + 1.5V = 3.0V. This makes a lamp shine more brightly.
2. Most lamps are made to work at a voltage of 3V or less. This means that they will only work with a maximum of two 1.5V batteries. If a third 1.5V battery is added it will raise the pushing power to 4.5V and this will burn out the lamp.
3. The voltage at which a bulb will work is marked on the casing. Some larger lamps have a voltage of 4.5V and can be used with three batteries in a line.

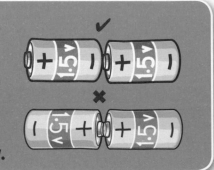

A

Which pairs of batteries allow electricity to flow? Tick the boxes.

A ☐   B ☐

C ☐   D ☐

Using more lamps

Learning objective: To learn how the arrangement of lamps affects their brightness.

The wire in the filament of the lamps offers some resistance to the flow of the current. As the current pushes against this resistance it can make the filament so hot that it shines and comes 'on'. The way lamps are connected together in a circuit affects the way they shine.

Lamps in a row
When lamps are arranged in a row they are said to be in **series**. If two lamps are in series the resistance of one filament wire adds to the resistance of the second and the current is slowed down. This means two lamps do not shine as brightly as a single lamp.

Lamps side by side
Lamps can be arranged side by side by connecting each one to the battery and switch. The lamps arranged in this way are said to be in **parallel**. The resistance of one filament does not add to the resistance of the other filament in this arrangement so both lamps shine as if they were in the circuit on their own.

DEFINITION

resistance The property of an electrical conductor that slows down the current of electricity passing through it.

B

One of arrangements A, B and C shines more dimly than the other two. Which is it?

A

B

C

Street lamps are arranged side by side in a circuit so if one goes out the rest stay lit.

Answers

Page 6
canine – tearing
molar – grinding
incisor – cutting

Page 7
Plaque is a sticky **coating** that covers the teeth. **Microbes** live in it and make **acid** that rots your **teeth**. When you **clean** your teeth you remove the acid and **plaque** and keep your teeth **healthy**.

Page 8
chicken leg – meat and fish
chips and peas – fruit and vegetables
bread and butter – fats, starches and sugar
apple – fruit and vegetables
bread – carbohydrates

Page 9
fish – helps you grow
bread – gives you energy
orange – keeps you healthy
If you eat more fatty and sugary food than meat , fruit and vegetables you are not eating healthily.

Page 11
1. You should move your finger from the root upwards to all parts of the plant to show the path of water.
2. You should move your finger from the leaf to all the other parts of the plant to show the path of food.

Page 12
1. The plant without leaves had not grown as well as the one with leaves. It was shorter.
2. The leaves need light to make them turn green.
3. The plant had grown to try to find light.

Page 13
1. That too much or too little water can kill plants and there is a certain amount of water at which plants grow best (which is around 15cm^3 per day for cress seedlings).
2. Warmth makes plants grow faster.

Page 14
1. Stone and brick 2. Wood, plastic and pottery. 3. Metal, rubber, glass. 4. Wooden table, fabric or plastic tablecloth, pottery or plastic plate, metal knife and fork

Page 15
1. Hard, rough, dull 2. Glass 3. A, D, E and F

Page 16
1. B has the most wear and A has the least.
2. C, D, A, B

Page 17
1. A and C 2. B, D and E 3. No
4. B lets through most water because there is a big spot on the towel. E and D have smaller spots.

Page 18

basalt – F, chalk – E, granite – B, slate – G, sandstone – A, marble – C, limestone – D

Page 19

1. Granite – non-porous, limestone – porous, sandstone – porous, basalt – non-porous
2. Non-porous because it keeps the rain from coming through the roof.

Page 20

1. Sand 2. Clay 3. By using a different sieve that only lets clay through and keeps silt in the sieve.

Page 21

1. A 40cm^3, B 57cm^3, C 29cm^3 2. C 3. B

Page 22

1. They repel each other. 2. They attract each other. 3. They repel each other.
4. Attract 5. Repel

Page 23

1. C 2. A 3. C

Page 24

1. A will squash, B will not change. 2. A will stretch a little, B will stretch a little.

Page 25

1. about 5cm 2. about 30cm

Page 26

Torch A

Page 27

Clear plastic T, window glass T, wood O, water T, frosted glass TR, brick O, cardboard O, metal O, greaseproof paper TR, orange juice O

Page 28

A 13.00 B 09.00 C 10.00

Page 29

1. 15cm 2. A – false, B – true, C – true

Page 30

Shin bone, kneecap, thigh bone, pelvis, spine

Page 31

slug – water skeleton
frog and snake – skeleton of bone
shrimp and spider – skeleton of armour

Page 32

The biceps gets shorter, harder and fatter.

Page 33

Makes the bones, joints, muscles and heart strong, prevents people becoming overweight.

Page 34

A is a habitat, B is a mini habitat, C and D are micro habitats.

Page 35

1. It would die because there is not enough light for it to survive.

Answers

2. It would be dashed on the rocks by the waves or be swept out to sea and die.

Page 36
1. Insects – D, spiders – A, fish – G, amphibians – E, reptiles – B, birds – F mammals – C
2. Humans belong to the mammal group.

Page 37
A – Horse chestnut, B – beech, C – ash, D – holly, E – oak, F – lime

Page 38
1. lettuce (or any other plant food) > human
2. grain (or grass) > chicken (or sheep, cattle) > human

Page 40

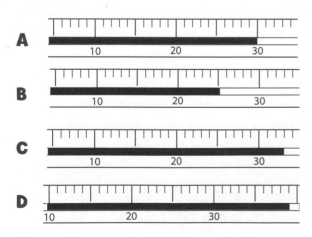

Page 41
1.

Time from start (minutes)	Temperature (°C)
0	35
1	30
2	25
3	20
4	20

2. Because the water has cooled to room temperature.
3.

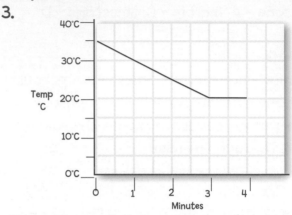

Page 42
1. The cup shows how the water cools without the material. This makes the test fair by showing how each material affects cooling.
2. B – wool
3. C – aluminium foil

Page 43
1. C – the steel spoon
2. The butter would melt because aluminium is a metal like steel and metals are good conductors.
3. The heat passes quickly from the oven to the food and speeds up cooking.
Pan handles are made of insulating materials like wood or plastic so hands are not burned.

Page 44
1. A – 10cm³, B – 30cm³   2. 40cm³

Page 45
1. The same volume of liquid is used and the slope is kept at the same angle.

2. A – vegetable oil, B – treacle, C – water

Page 46
1. A, C, B, D
2. B and D
3. 650°C.

Page 47
The molten rock **flowing** down the **side** of a volcano is a **liquid** and may be as **hot** as 1200°C. It cools as it moves **away** and when it reaches **600°C** it stops flowing and becomes **solid** rock. The **freezing** point of the rock is 600°C.

Page 48
1. Sugar, instant coffee granules, salt
2. Some substances in the tea leaves dissolve in the water but the leaf does not.

Page 49
1. The sand grains will stay in the filter paper because they are too big to go through the holes. The sugar will pass through because it has dissolved in the water.
2. You can tell when sugar and salt are dissolved in water by the taste of the water.
3. Yes. The holes let the dissolved substance pass through but keep the leaves in the bag.

Page 50
A – 3, B – 5, C – 8, D – 4

Page 51
Sandpaper, velvet, newspaper, plastic sheet.

Page 52
1. Fastest – A, slowest – B
2. By repeating the experiment up to five times more.

Page 53
1. C 2. B 3. 7 seconds

Page 54
motor – provides movement
wire – conducts electricity
buzzer – makes a sound
switch – controls the flow of electricity

Page 55
No. There is a gap in the circuit.

Page 56
1. steel spoon - conductor, wooden spoon – insulator, copper pipe – conductor, plastic comb – insulator
2. It is an insulator. If it was a conductor the lamp would light when there was no other material in the gap.

Page 57
When the tube is tipped so the left side goes down, the ball bearing rolls onto the ends of the wires and electricity can flow through it from one wire to the next.

Page 58
A and D should be ticked.

Page 59
B

Index